Not I
Sebastian Castillo

word west press | brooklyn, ny

isbn: 978-1-7334663-5-6

published by word west in brooklyn, ny.

first us edition 2020.
printed in the usa.

www.wordwest.co

cover: ava wolf
author illustration: gina lerman
interior design: word west

"Order leads to all the virtues! But what leads to order?"

—Georg Christoph Licthenberg, *The Waste Books*

"Speech / is a mouth."

—Robert Creeley, "The Language"

"For there was nothing in the world left for us to talk about—in fact, one could have argued that there never was anything to talk about from the beginning, and that the history of our talking was exactly that: the history of us talking."

—Pamela Lu, *Pamela: A Novel*

"You turn into a clown because you feel more and more like putting on a clown suit."

—Chelsey Minnis, "Clown"

"You say something you like, so you say it again."

—Ron Padgett, misquoting Gertrude Stein

"But people didn't understand what I meant, as usual, when I say something they don't understand it, for what I say doesn't mean that I said what I said, he said, I thought. I say something, he said, I thought, and I'm saying something completely different, thus I've spent my entire life in misunderstandings, in nothing but misunderstandings, he said, I thought. We are, to put it precisely, born into misunderstanding and never escape this condition of misunderstanding as long as we live, we can squirm and twist as much as we like, it doesn't help. But everyone can see this, he said, I thought, for everyone says something repeatedly and is misunderstood, this is the only point where everyone understands everybody else, he said, I thought."

—Thomas Bernhard, *The Loser*

"Did you think of listening to something else? We are all talkers / It is true, but underneath the talk lies / The moving and not wanting to be moved, the loose / Meaning, untidy and simple like a threshing floor."

—John Ashbery, "Soonest Mended"

NOTE ON THE TEXT

The 25 most common verbs in the English language, according to the *Oxford English Dictionary*, are:

be	want
have	give
do	use
say	find
get	tell
make	ask
go	work
know	seem
take	feel
see	try
come	leave
think	call
look	

There are 12 verb tenses in the English language, some say.

CONTENTS

SIMPLE PRESENT.

I.

I am Sebastian.

I have much to address.

I do words.

I say good things badly.

I get art.

I make toast.

I go to the park.

I know one or two things.

I take very little from people.

I see what you did there.

I come with baggage.

I think this is a bad idea.

I look at cats in my neighbor's window.

I want the money.

I give money to my friends.

I use toilet paper every day.

I find most facts interesting.

I tell people about kissing.

I ask for your forgiveness.

I work in a lazy way.

I seem awkward.

I feel normal.

I try occasionally.

I leave my house.

I call my mother.

II.

I am right over here.

I have so many sentences.

I do grammar.

I say different things to different people.

I get a worthless prize for it.

I make garbage bags with fancy logos on the front.

I go hardly.

I know when to shut up.

I take my losses where I can.

I see the future as a long, dim line.

I come out of it dead.

I think that's what happens.

I look at my fortune.

I want to feed crumbs to my enemies.

I give a shit.

I use sentences to my advantage.

I find that I like getting languagey with it.

I tell you to stay right where you are.

I ask lubricating questions.

I work on myself.

I seem robotic.

I feel like someone has poisoned me.

I try to get over those tawdry moments in life.

I leave the theater alone.

I call me what I want.

SIMPLE PAST.

I.

I was late to work.

I had no friends.

I did ugly.

I said so.

I got sick to my stomach.

I made the rounds in my pre-owned hazmat suit.

I went with the original plan.

I knew very little about her.

I took beers from your fridge.

I saw smoke in that room.

I came to.

I thought you were my friend.

I looked out for the cops.

I wanted love.

I gave away your childhood toys.

I used you.

I found it a drab affair.

I told you about him.

I asked for too much.

I worked on this quickly.

I seemed out of sorts.

I felt depressed.

I tried, failed, and then failed worse.

I left my family for good.

I called and you didn't pick up.

II.

I was thirsty.

I had my private bucket to fill with what I wanted.

I did it wrong.

I said as much.

I got the winning numbers.

I made antiques for the future.

I went off with them to make trouble.

I knew that it would end unsatisfactorily.

I took a chance, either way.

I saw myself for the first time every day.

I came to the award ceremony underdressed.

I thought no one would notice me.

I looked for reasons to live with discretion.

I wanted…I don't know.

I gave myself the appropriate time.

I used a rusted flashlight to guide myself
through the bedchamber.

I found the uselessness of treasure.

I told jokes to pass the day.

I asked for an extension.

I worked without pay.

I seemed to care less and less.

I felt buoyant and clear.

I tried looking you up.

I left the gala on fire.

I called on a number of experts to no avail.

SIMPLE FUTURE.

I.

I will be something very small.

I will grow into jealousy.

I will do what has to be done.

I will say plain, nasty things.

I will get what I want.

I will make do.

I will go to the poet's moon.

I will know too much about the government.

I will take out the trash like a hung-over dancer.

I will see Atlantis, but not for a long time.

I will come when called upon by my lord, unfortunately.

I will think about serious illness.

I will look up my own skirt.

I will want more when I'm rich and lonely.

I will give coal to both friends and traitors.

I will use your porcelain bathtub now.

I will find the words you've been hiding
from me.

I will tell your secrets to nationally distributed
magazines.

I will ask for nothing in return.

I will work until I can do nothing.

I will seem suspicious, but please trust me.

I will feel that terrible pressure.

I will try a new path.

I will leave you with this.

I will call the police on myself.

II.

I will be ready tomorrow.

I will grow something hearty and nourishing.

I will do that tomorrow, too.

I will say that I found the soirée unimpressive.

I will get what you require when the time comes.

I will make poison for myself.

I will go to the store without a list.

I will know exactly what I need.

I will take power, but promise to disperse it immediately.

I will see after the results come in.

I will come to a feeble ending.

I will think in the past tense.

I will look up to no one.

I will want lunch any time of day.

I will give you that which you seek, after payment.

I will use my erudition because it's naughty.

I will find that I need to adjust my light bulb.

I will tell on no one.

I will ask for no one.

I will work with no one.

I will seem cold and dry and past due.

I will feel that no one wants me around.

I will try to get a different job.

I will leave without notice.

I will call my own references.

PRESENT CONTINUOUS.

I.

I am being serious here.

I am having a baby.

I am doing pornography.

I am saying—that's fine!

I am getting frustrated.

I am making this happen.

I am going to the ego circus.

I am [know]

I am taking it all away from you.

I am seeing something develop here.

I am coming to dinner with my own napkins.

I am thinking against myself.

I am looking for a way out.

~~I am [want]~~

I am giving this away for free, after all.

I am using you.

I am finding out that it's all true.

I am telling you to stop.

I am asking you so nicely.

I am working on my novel.

I am [seem]

I am feeling that lump again.

I am trying very hard.

I am leaving the country for good.

I am calling you out.

II.

I am being stupid here.

I am having the time of my life.

I am doing all the wrong things.

I am saying it again.

I am getting in the way of myself.

I am making art.

I am going out the back door of the world.

~~I am [know]~~

I am taking a left turn.

I am seeing that I was right all along.

I am coming to the celebratory bon fire.

I am thinking for too long.

I am looking for the destroyed library.

~~I am {want}~~

I am giving you a second chance.

I am using up all my time here writing things like this.

I am finding that there isn't much to do.

I am telling you in advance, at least.

I am asking you to please listen carefully.

I am working on my new gun.

~~I am [seem]~~

I am feeling the weather again.

I am trying to solve this problem as quickly as possible.

I am leaving the cards on the table.

I am calling it.

PAST CONTINUOUS.

I.

I was being Sebastian every day that summer.

I was having a bit of a laugh.

I was doing something special.

I was saying that we should be done with this.

I was getting paid.

I was making an elaborate dinner.

I was going to stop myself.

I was known to get out of hand.

I was taking my time.

I was seeing what was out there.

I was coming clean.

I was thinking about coming.

I was looking under the desk.

I was wanting a little thanks, that's all.

I was giving a little kiss.

I was using drugs.

I was finding that it didn't help.

I was telling you about this already.

I was asking him if it was okay about the scorched-earth thing.

I was working the night shift.

I was seeming like I didn't want this anymore.

I was feeling lonely.

I was trying to feel spiritual.

I was leaving my life in a dusty box in the basement.

I was calling you earlier.

II.

I was being a tad coy.

I was having a difficult time finishing.

I was doing it all out of order.

I was saying to her that it might be a bit bland, in the end.

I was getting accolades I didn't deserve.

I was making myself a Molotov cocktail with a bit of mint.

I was going over the speed limit.

I was known for my haircut.

I was taking the rigged dice out of your hand.

I was seeing that it was much easier than anticipated.

I was coming from another time zone.

I was thinking about emotional truancy.

I was looking for an easy way out.

I was wanting to know my limits.

I was giving you a hard time.

I was using words like "ablative."

I was finding out how little others thought about these things.

I was telling myself in the mirror.

I was asking the questions that needed answers.

I was working on a plan bound to fail.

I was seeming into it.

I was feeling like, okay, I'm ready now.

I was trying to convince myself of something important.

I was leaving clues for you to find me.

I was calling your name in the chamber
play.

FUTURE CONTINUOUS.

I.

~~I will be [be]~~

I will be having the ten-course meal, thank you.

I will be doing what you ask me to.

I will be saying words of praise about your mediocre performance.

I will be getting surgery tomorrow.

I will be making an omelet with shells and other detritus.

I will be going to the theater with mother.

I will be known for my sad charisma.

I will be taking my business elsewhere.

I will be seeing you at your idiot son's
wedding.

I will be coming down the mountain.

I will be thinking about poetry.

I will be looking for answers.

I will be wanting a cookie.

I will be giving all of my energy to damage
the zoo.

I will be using the manual to get through it.

I will be finding that it's wrong.

I will be telling her that I'm wrong.

I will be asking about the coupons, the discounts.

I will be working tomorrow night, again.

I will be seeming like I'm not sure what I'm saying.

I will be feeling sorry for myself.

I will be trying out new clothes.

I will be leaving my knives to the lonely children.

I will be calling out of work for good.

II.

~~I will [be]~~

I will be having a breakdown.

I will be doing more harm than good.

I will be saying the words incorrectly.

I will be getting a high-five from the
neighborhood.

I will be making out like a bandit.

I will be going out of my gourd.

I will be known for more or less nothing.

I will be taking a shit on company time.

I will be seeing you never.

I will be coming down with something
serious.

I will be thinking about the moment where
I can pack things up for good.

I will be looking forward to it, maybe.

I will be wanting to speak without a frame.

I will be giving a rat's ass.

I will be using my acumen and fiscal dexterity.

I will be finding out what you've redacted from your progeny.

I will be telling no one.

I will be asking for your manager's head.

I will be working on this with you.

I will be seeming calm.

I will be feeling like we've accomplished something together.

I will be trying out for the part.

I will be leaving my possessions at the
bottom of a river.

I will be calling you when I'm bored.

PRESENT PERFECT.

I.

I have been here before.

I have had enough already, man.

I have done nothing wrong.

I have said all that I can say.

I have gotten suspended from literature.

I have made something for you.

I have gone to indecent lengths, it's true.

I have known about it for a long time
without telling you.

I have taken the mantle from seminal figures.

I have seen and unseen nudity.

I have come for the awards you didn't deserve.

I have thought long and soft about it.

I have looked into the matter concerning your premature termination.

I have wanted you for a season and a half.

I have given you the painful edits.

I have used clinical methods.

I have found the opposite of God.

I have told him repeatedly.

I have asked for a raise.

I have worked for zero years.

I have seemed better.

I have felt the same.

I have tried to forget.

I have left the building.

I have called you bad things on purpose.

II.

I have been dishonest with you.

I have had a bad day.

I have done something that I don't understand.

I have said this to you before.

I have gotten a raw deal.

I have made out like a thief in the night.

I have gone too far, I know.

I have known about my mistakes for a long time.

I have taken precaution with my words.

I have seen how the gamble pays off.

I have come to understand something I shouldn't.

I have thought about using my abacus on unsuspecting strangers.

I have looked both ways while crossing the street.

I have wanted a name change.

I have given the lawyers their money.

I have used the local mafia to great success.

I have found the answer.

I have told on myself.

I have asked superior questions.

I have worked on my language.

I have seemed to have a fruitful time with it.

I have felt you move away from me.

I have tried to come up with something new.

I have left the remains of my bungled attempts.

I have called on the jury to rank my character.

PAST PERFECT

I.

I had been there before.

I had had enough, again.

I had done something which could not be reversed.

I had said only positive things about my enemies.

I had gotten a D+.

I had made my bed.

I had gone to the boss' funeral.

I had known better than to speak.

I had taken the rations to my commune.

I had seen ancient ruins, and furnished ruins.

I had come out to the retirement party.

I had thought it was the end of time, finally.

I had looked over the ocean's sliced horizon.

I had wanted better eyesight.

I had given myself a religious tattoo.

I had used the occult arbiter.

I had found some money in a ditch.

I had told the authorities.

I had asked if there would be a reward for my good manners.

I had worked on this brain for at least a century.

I had seemed beyond repair.

I had felt like a million bucks.

I had tried to forget all of that.

I had left my wallet in the cab.

I had called an old friend who was dead.

II.

I had been ill due to my own machinations.

I had had it up to here!

I had done the things which I had been told to do.

I had said to the doctor that, really, I'm fine.

I had gotten the best grades on my illness.

I had made it.

I had gone to my little hole.

I had known better, but behaved against my best interest.

I had taken pills, etc.

I had seen the light, or not.

I had come to the right place, either way.

I had thought of myself last.

I had looked through your dresser drawer.

I had wanted a big steak.

I had given up, and that's it.

I had used up all my remaining resources.

I had found the correct answer to a decades-unsolved riddle.

I had told the president.

I had asked if I could have the rest of my life off.

I had worked toward these declarations.

I had seemed worse for wear.

I had felt my manners shore up my criminal instincts.

I had tried to lift you.

I had left small bits of myself all over the place.

I had called upon the forces of evil.

FUTURE PERFECT

I.

I will have been corrected.

I will have had to make public apologies.

I will have done nothing out of the ordinary.

I will have said things unconvincingly.

I will have gotten a fat check for my crimes.

I will have made a private castle in the king's basement.

I will have gone back to clown school.

I will have known the depressed clown of lore.

I will have taken the answer key while the teacher wasn't looking.

I will have seen the end of the road.

I will have come off the wrong way.

I will have thought through my problems with diffidence, holding a wet bathroom key.

I will have looked through my pockets.

I will have wanted a public retraction.

I will have given my master a rotten egg.

I will have used up my long-term energy.

I will have found that deeper readings yield confounding results.

I will have told my teachers as much.

I will have asked for a larger canvas.

I will have worked through problems that didn't exist.

I will have seemed gigantic.

I will have felt puffy.

I will have tried to work out for the rest of my life.

I will have left the academy.

I will have called for a permanent hiatus.

II.

I will have been dead for a long time when you read this.

I will have had a beautiful life.

I will have done things with charity and grace.

I will have said quotes.

I will have gotten a medal of honor from the void.

I will have made pretty objects out of boring mistakes.

I will have gone to the movies.

I will have known thirty unpopular poets.

I will have taken it for granted.

I will have seen hours of plants fighting to win.

I will have come to a great understanding.

I will have thought that I knew it all.

I will have looked sick and humid.

I will have wanted wanton love, occasionally.

I will have given my trust to robber barons.

I will have used a condom.

I will have found fossils in dumpsters.

I will have told useless stories to the next generation.

I will have asked stupid questions.

I will have worked at a guitar store.

I will have seemed bloated.

I will have felt ugly, too.

I will have tried every combination on the safe.

I will have left a note to my friends.

I will have called it the past.

PRESENT PERFECT CONTINUOUS

I.

~~I have been [be]~~

I have been having a swell time of it.

I have been doing the chores for no thanks
at all.

I have been saying pithy aphorisms for the
sake of genius.

I have been getting a lot of flak for it.

I have been making a goulash for you.

I have been going on and on about it.

~~I have been [know]~~

I have been taking credit.

I have been seeing your progress.

I have been coming up with dastardly
solutions.

I have been thinking about exploding my
mouth.

I have been looking out for your family's
estate.

I have been wanting to send you a vaguely
coquettish letter.

I have been giving so much and taking so little.

I have been using devices since my youth.

I have been finding things with the map you gave me.

I have been telling lies to my brothers.

I have been asking the priest to come out of his priest box.

I have been working on my religion.

~~I have been [seem]~~

I have been feeling down again.

I have been trying to get out of here.

I have been leaving a breadcrumb trail for
my enemies.

I have been calling on wolves.

II.

I have been [be]

I have been having a tedious experience.

I have been doing the most that one can do.

I have been saying a little prayer.

I have been getting no response.

I have been making it up as I go along.

I have been going to the cemetery on weekends.

I have been [know]

I have been taking liberties with the truth.

I have been seeing changes in my behavior.

I have been coming forward with slander.

I have been thinking about canceling my subscription to myself.

I have been looking for other options.

I have been wanting to say goodbye to you.

I have been giving the most my effort can declare.

I have been using personality-enhancing software.

I have been finding delicious quotations to use in moments of doubt.

I have been telling a story about someone I've never met.

I have been asking you to keep up with me.

I have been working to craft a convincing protagonist with some issues.

~~I have been [seem]~~

I have been feeling that the job is not yet done.

I have been trying to mitigate the effects of my words on your understanding of me.

I have been leaving work early for some years now.

I have been calling in a bomb threat.

PAST PERFECT CONTINUOUS

I.

~~I had been [be]~~

I had been having indigestion.

I had been doing all the bountiful things.

I had been saying something embarrassingly true.

I had been getting ahead, despite my laziness.

I had been making the best of a bad situation.

I had been going over the rule book upside down.

~~I had been [know]~~

I had been taking supplies from the office.

I had been seeing how my plan was falling apart.

I had been coming to terms with my failure.

I had been thinking about changing course, but no.

I had been looking for the escape hatch.

I had been wanting senescent results.

I had been giving myself perfect marks.

I had been using my private rubric.

I had been finding my public self.

I had been telling my colleagues how to
steal from the fridge.

I had been asking you what you think about
my protocol.

I had been working towards nothing but a
smug ambivalence.

~~I had been [seem]~~

I had been feeling like a cross sprouted in
my stomach.

I had been trying to give myself medical attention, or any kind of attention.

I had been leaving myself slowly.

I had been calling for a new way to direct my gaze.

II.

~~I had been [be]~~

I had been having leftovers.

I had been doing the numbers and it wasn't looking good.

I had been saying this for eternity.

I had been getting a stipend for work I promised I'd complete.

I had been making illegible scribbles in the sand.

I had been going away at every opportunity.

~~I had been [know]~~

I had been taking the requisite bathroom breaks.

I had been seeing visions of a future without content.

I had been coming up with theories that explained very little.

I had been thinking that I needed to behave differently.

I had been looking up better words in the dictionary.

I had been wanting to scream at you politely.

I had been giving away my passwords.

I had been using an alias to check into life.

I had been finding that, at best, the answer
is inconclusive.

I had been telling jokes to my executioner.

I had been asking for a side of hot sauce.

I had been working on my self-esteem.

I had been [seem]

I had been feeling low.

I had been trying out a new outfit.

I had been leaving my social security card on the street.

I had been calling, and calling.

FUTURE PERFECT CONTINUOUS

I.

I will have been [be]

I will have been having a heart attack.

I will have been doing pushups naked on
the beach of your dreams.

I will have been saying the most banal
things for the rest of my life.

I will have been getting royalty payments
for my personality.

I will have been making bread in a stone
oven.

I will have been going to the parking lot of my mind.

I will have been [know]

I will have been taking one for the team.

I will have been seeing how my body heals itself with something different than before.

I will have been coming to an inane conclusion.

I will have been thinking with symphonic grandeur.

I will have been looking with the eyes of a shepherd.

I will have been wanting a permanent bath.

I will have been giving my fingers the day off.

I will have been using the complimentary toothbrush.

I will have been finding bodies in yesterday's foxholes.

I will have been telling a story with the end chopped off.

I will have been asking the narrator to stop now.

I will have been working with an experienced team of vagabonds to appraise the contents of your vault.

~~I will have been [seem]~~

I will have been feeling a breezy sangfroid.

I will have been trying to compose myself accordingly.

I will have been leaving my shoes by the door.

I will have been calling for an insurrection against our friendship.

II.

I will have been [be]

I will have been a good boy.

I will have been doing the daily tasks
around the house.

I will have been saying my obituary in
advance.

I will have been getting over what to say.

I will have been making a compilation of
things I wished I never thought about.

I will have been going into retirement.

I will have been [know]

I will have been taking your time.

I will have been seeing you to the door.

I will have been coming down with something
permanent.

I will have been thinking about the things
I'd done with aplomb.

I will have been looking with damaged
vision for the majority of my life.

I will have been wanting a pot of gold.

I will have been giving you a piece of my mind.

I will have been using the dim tools afforded to me.

I will have been finding new ways to say the same things.

I will have been telling a tale of romance and murder.

I will have been asking to speak with you.

I will have been working toward resolution.

~~I will have been [seem]~~

I will have been feeling that it didn't come out right.

I will have been trying, despite this.

I will have been leaving the book on your desk.

I will have been calling for another chance.

ABOUT THE AUTHOR